MW00696087
the SWO
ROB
ROY
GENE E. VEITH story
JUDITH A. HUNT art

the SWORD of ROB ROY

ISBN# 1-930710-48-8

Veritas Press
1250 Belle Meade Drive
Lancaster, PA 17601

First edition

Veritas Press

The boy stared at the long piece of steel sitting in the glass box. He wanted to feel the glass, but his fingers hovered just above it. In his mind, he saw himself holding the steel in front of his buddies. Yet it was not a toy. It was the sword of Rob Roy.

The man who had wielded this sword was a hero of old Scotland, when the castles breathed and brave men wore kilts. His name was Rob Roy, and he started as a simple farmer and cattle rancher. His young son and daughters sometimes tromped in the fields with him, driving the herd. His wife watched

her husband toil, and she worked hard in their hatched hut. Some days he would stare from the field at her golden hair, and he would leave his work and go kiss her smiling lips. They all loved to be tired at the end of the day, and they thanked God for the work of their hands.

Some people want things without work. One such man, a Duke, lusted after land, especially Rob Roy's land. So by using some

tricks and lies, this Duke caught Rob Roy and put him in jail. The Duke took Rob Roy's cattle and money and home.

Sitting in jail, Rob Roy's mind was full of his family and lost freedom. He remembered playing with his children and holding his wife and working his land. The Duke's lies could not hold him in jail, so he figured out a plan for escape.

When the time was right, he sneaked out of jail and hid in the hills. The word of his

escape spread quickly among his clan, his Scottish tribe.

His wife and children joined him in the hills, and soon the call went from man to man, "Join Rob Roy to resist the Duke!"

They were all tired of this thieving Duke and longed for freedom. The Duke was enraged that these men were gathering in the hills and plotting to resist him.

He called his own men in armor and started hunting Rob Roy and his brave band. Rob Roy's men knew they were not pirates. They were protecting their families and lands. As the Bible says,

Riches from wickedness profit nothing: but goodness delivers from death.

Rob Roy raised his voice to his men. "We may die. But our people and land need protectors. You have made your choice. Go with God!" Some of his men had foils.

Some had big swords. Some had spears. A few had old guns. They prayed to God for help, as they hid in the trees by the road.

Days passed. Then the Duke's men came slowly along the forest road. They rode by with their noses high and their chests puffed out. From the trees, Rob Roy gave the call. His men jumped out and yelled at the enemy horses.

The horses were terrified, and Rob Roy's men cast their spears. Others swung their swords in the dim forest air, clashing and beating, sword upon sword.

Sword clanged on armor; shields clanked in surprise. A hail of gunfire filled the woods with smoke. One of the Duke's big men, a hulk in armor, grabbed Rob Roy. The man circled his ax in the air and growled,

"I will cleave your head and leave you dead!" The ax whistled in the air, but Rob Roy ducked. Rob Roy gripped his sword by the hilt and thrust its sharp point into a chink in his foe's armor. The man screamed with wide eyes and then collapsed to the dirt.

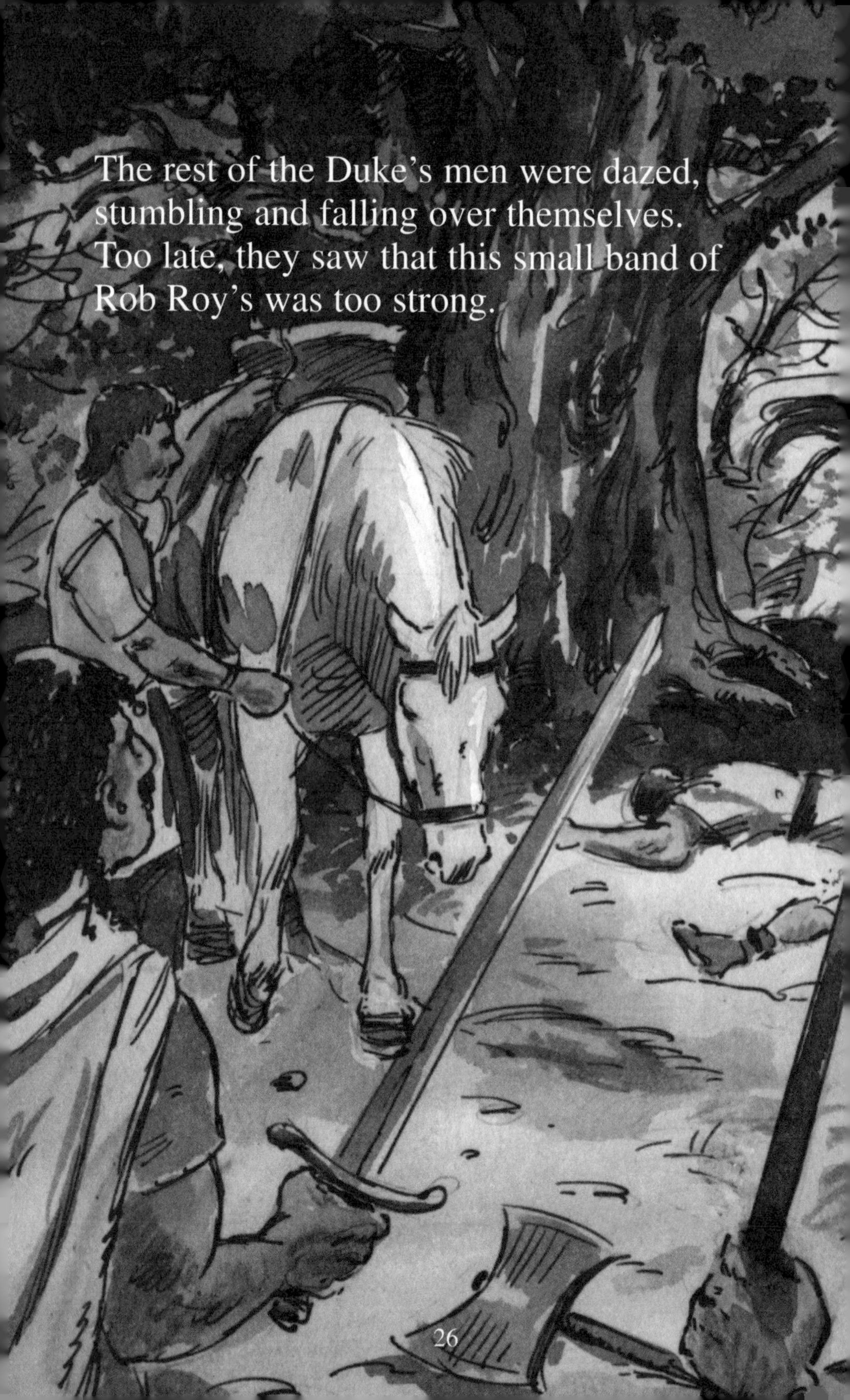

The rest of the Duke's men were dazed, stumbling and falling over themselves. Too late, they saw that this small band of Rob Roy's was too strong.

Finally, fear overtook the Duke's men, and they ran. They climbed back on their horses and made them run like the wind, back to the Duke. Rob Roy's clan roared with joy.

“We are just a wee lot of weak men,” shouted Rob Roy. “Aye, but God made us winners. ” For years after, Rob Roy’s clan hid in the hills. They played tricks on the Duke and

raided his plundered land. The Duke's men tried to catch them, but always in vain. In the end, Rob Roy's clan spoiled the Duke's plans to rule the land.

"Rejoice!" the wise men told the Scottish girls and boys. "God has granted us freedom once more."

In the case is a bit of drab steel, rusting along the edges. It is an old sword, but it is not a toy. It is the sword of Rob Roy.